Rebecca Colby

Caroline Bonne-Müller

Beatrix and her Bunnies

The Story of Beatrix Potter

To Kathleen Rushall, who ensures my own stories live on forever – R.C.

For Mama, who read me Beatrix Potter's stories – C.B.M.

This is a picture book based on the life of Beatrix Potter.

First published 2021 by Nosy Crow Ltd
The Crow's Nest, 14 Baden Place
Crosby Row, London SE1 1YW
www.nosycrow.com

ISBN 978 1 83994 093 4 (HB)
ISBN 978 1 83994 107 8 (PB)

A CIP catalogue record for this book is available from the British Library.

Printed in China

Papers used by Nosy Crow are made from wood grown in sustainable forests.

1 3 5 7 9 8 6 4 2 (HB)
1 3 5 7 9 8 6 4 2 (PB)

Rebecca Colby

Caroline Bonne-Müller

Beatrix and her Bunnies

The Story of Beatrix Potter

Once there was a little girl named Beatrix.
She lived in a house in London that was
large and sometimes lonely.

Even though she had lots of animals that she cared for very much . . .

snails and salamanders . . .

birds and bats . . .

frogs and hedgehogs . . .

none of them was the perfect playmate.

"If only frogs could play leapfrog," thought Beatrix, "or hedgehogs could play hopscotch."

More than anything, she longed for a special friend.

Beatrix searched everywhere for a playmate.

When she visited the countryside with her family, she would hunt through the bushes for wild rabbits whose black eyes flashed with fun.

But whenever Beatrix tried to start a game, they bounded away across the fields, leaving her feeling as lonely as ever.

Then, one day, Beatrix met Benjamin. Benjamin was different. He wiggled his whiskers in a way that could only mean, "Hello, how are you?"

And when she brought him home, he hopped around after her as though he already knew how to play 'Follow the Leader'.

As they curled up by the fire that evening,
Beatrix had a feeling that she and
Benjamin would be friends forever.

In the mornings, Benjamin twitched his nose as if to say, "Time for a walk!" Then in the afternoons, when he heard the tea bell, he would race Beatrix upstairs for their buttered toast.

All day long, Beatrix drew pictures of Benjamin.

Her father said her drawing was getting better – and Beatrix knew it was true. She sketched and sketched until she drew every single hair on Benjamin's tail just right!

But bunnies don't live forever.

As the years went by, Beatrix noticed that Benjamin's hoppity-hops weren't as high as they used to be . . .

and his naps by the fire were getting longer and longer, until, one day . . .

Benjamin died.

The large house in London
became lonely once again.

Drawing and painting helped Beatrix feel a little better, but the city was so grey and gloomy.

When she visited the countryside, it was easier to fill the pages of her sketchbook with flowers, mushrooms and colourful creatures. But memories of Benjamin still hopped through her head.

Then, a short while later, Beatrix met Peter. He wiggled his whiskers in a "hello" that reminded her of Benjamin.

Peter didn't listen for the tea bell to ring. He rang bells himself . . . and played a tambourine . . .

and when visitors came with their children to see Beatrix's family, Peter would jump through hoops!

Children adored him. And they gave Beatrix an idea . . .

She picked up her pen and thought about the countryside
she loved – the fir tree forests, the blackberry bushes,
the cottage gardens . . . and about her bunnies.

As she scribbled, she drew pictures, too. By the time
Beatrix finished, her work was eight pages long.
It was the story of a rabbit named Peter, who had
a cousin called Benjamin.

She thought that if she showed the story to publishers,
they could make it into a book and print lots of copies,
so that many children could read it.

That way, her bunnies could live forever.

Beatrix Potter

But not everyone loved this story
about Peter the way Beatrix did.

The publishers said things like . . .

"We don't want stories about rabbits."
"Sorry, we don't think people will buy this."
They all said, "No."
Not one publisher wanted to make her story into a book.

But Beatrix refused to give up.

She asked again . . .

and again . . .

until, at last, one publisher said, “Yes!” He laughed out loud at Peter’s adventures and decided this story would make a wonderful book!

Peter Rabbit
CONTRACT

Before long, people were buying beautiful little copies of *The Tale of Peter Rabbit* from shops. Then more and more copies sold – all around the world. Soon, Beatrix knew that lots of people did love her bunnies.

In fact, so many people bought her books that Beatrix had enough money to leave the house in London that was large and sometimes lonely . . .

. . . and move to a cottage in the countryside that was cosy and always cheery and filled with lots of animal friends.

Through her stories, Beatrix shared these friends with the world, too . . .

. . . and as she grew older, there was something else Beatrix wanted to share – the countryside she loved so much.

She worked hard to make sure that the green valleys around her weren't filled with houses and that the sheep had plenty of grass to graze on.

Beatrix gave away all her land to friends who promised to look after it, so that the countryside could be enjoyed by everyone.

Like her bunnies, she will be remembered forever.

Author's Note

Beatrix Potter was born in 1866 to a wealthy family. She lived in London with her parents, a younger brother named Bertram and several servants. Bertram went to school, but Beatrix studied at home with a governess and spent a lot of time on her own, drawing and painting.

When Beatrix grew up, she became friends with her governess Annie Moore, who had a son named Noel. Once, when Noel was ill, Beatrix wrote him a special story about a family of rabbits. This story became *The Tale of Peter Rabbit*. Noel loved it and, after many disappointing rejections, it was finally published as a book in 1902. More stories followed, and characters such as Jemima Puddle-Duck, Mrs Tiggy-Winkle and Benjamin Bunny soon became favourites all around the world. Beatrix wrote and illustrated 23 animal tales, which sold millions of copies and made her one of the world's best-loved authors.

Beatrix used the money from her book sales to buy farms and land in the Lake District. She worked closely with the National Trust to protect the beautiful countryside around her. When Beatrix died at the age of 77, she gave the National Trust 15 farms and more than 4,000 acres of land. This included her home, Hill Top Farm, which you can still visit today.